CW00407125

IF FEELINGS WERE WORDS

IF FEELINGS WERE

WORDS

JIM LAW

CONTENTS

PREFACE

What started as a bunch of therapeutic, hand-written scribbles in a composition book turned into something more as time went on. Spanning about three years from separation, subsequent divorce, grieving, dating, growing, and learning to love again, these pages document a journey of thoughts, feelings, and experiences. To love, lose, and love again has reminded me how life truly is a beautiful adventure.

I
PART ONE

She Who Broke my Heart (The End)

FINI

They sat in the courthouse, talking, a slight smile upon his face as he watched her speak to him like she used to. Her legs were crossed and turned toward him. An outside observer would think they were a couple getting to know each other, or very much in love. But the setting betrayed that thought. They were there to end that which they had built together. The hearing was quick; it was approved. They left the courthouse and walked to the corner. She asked him to walk with her to the car; she would take him to his. He obliged her, if only to hear her voice for a few minutes longer.

They talked about teenagers learning to drive and other small things. When they arrived at his car, they looked at each other. He reached out to hug her, put his arm around her, his head on the back of hers. Her face buried in the cradle of his arm. He kissed her on the back of her neck like he had done so many times before. She kissed his arm.

"I love you," he said as he choked back tears.

"I love you, too," she replied.

"Take care of yourself, okay," he said.

"Okay. Don't be a stranger," she said as he opened the car door.

Walking to his car, the tears began to leak from his left eye first, and then his right. He could feel the emotion swell within him. The tears streaked down his face as memories flashed and faded. The road blurred in the rush of what was. He cried the whole drive home, with Ed Sheeran playing in the background.

What was once his happiness, his life, is Fini.

MY RING

I opened my drawer to get briefs and socks, the shower warming in the background. I was rustling through the drawer to avoid boxer briefs on this hot spring day. I counted one, two, three pairs in hand before finding the pair I wanted to wear. Laundry must be done, I thought. Lifting the dark blue underwear exposed a symbol of my previous life. A symbol of continuation. A reminder of the commitment that once was. The once-worn, never-removed, platinum band that had once blessed my finger. I felt overcome with emotion, seeing it there, motionless. How cold it must be, hidden from sight. What it once symbolized now gone, but not forgotten. A feeling of nakedness tingled through the ring finger of my left hand, missing the ring's presence. My eyes and finger were not cooperating. To feel its presence or absence, seeing its place in the drawer, lonely and tucked away. It felt as if two people stood there, the man who once wore that ring and the man who was staring at it, imagining how that other man's life was.

I closed the drawer and turned towards the sound of the shower, a tear falling from each eye. Suddenly, the rush of what was and what had been collided within my soul. I missed the life that was symbolized by my ring.

EMPTY

It was a quiet night at home that Friday. The gentle pitter-patter of rain outside was soothing. The dinner he prepared looked to be for two, but only one plate sat upon the cold, beige counter. A glass of chardonnay sat next to that empty plate. The aroma of lemon herb chicken wafted through the house. The senses were engaged with the sound of the rain, the smell of the dinner, the taste of the wine, the sight of the empty plate, and the subtle, mixed feeling of comfort and loneliness.

He placed a piece of the moist, tender, aromatic chicken breast on the plate, slowly sipped the chardonnay, and listened to the rain. Broccoli joined the chicken. What was empty was now full. Sip. He ate the nourishing meal in what would be silence were it not for that gentle rain. He looked around the kitchen and into the living room—empty of life. The ironies of the pictures on the wall were not lost on him. A framed, inspirational poster of "CHANGE." Beneath it, an image from a pleasant past: himself, a woman, and four children. The sand, dunes, and smiles projected happiness and beauty; change, the reminder of what seems inevitable.

He took his last sip of chardonnay and placed the empty glass next to the empty plate. The rain had stopped. The silence of the room was deafening. The void of sound, sight, and feeling weighed on him. He closed his eyes, lowered his head, and sadly took in the quiet and the change. His life was now empty.

LITTLE SPOON

She lay there next to him, facing away. The little spoon. His arm wrapped over her, his hand resting on her outer thigh. She had been distant; he sensed it. She still sighed in contentment at his touch. He kissed the back of her neck. She reached down to grab his hand, resting gently on her thigh, and drew it up to her chest, gripping it. How he longed for the days when she talked to him about anything. He knew, deep down, that something was not right. When he asked, he was prying, and when he didn't, he didn't care.

He could feel a deep conflict within her. He hoped he would survive the slow loss of the beautiful intimacy they had shared. He felt, knew in his soul, that something had changed in her, but what exactly he did not know.

She gripped his hand and wiggled her ass, snuggling more closely to him. Their legs intertwined, occupying as much space as they could, together. He sensed she might want him, but the emotional distance weighed heavily on him. Had he offered, they would probably have made love, but something was missing. He wanted to, but she barely spoke. She was expecting him to read her mind. Instead, he squeezed his little spoon and told her he loved her. She responded with the same. As he wished her good night and pleasant dreams, he felt her slip further away from him—his tangled little spoon.

REMNANTS OF YOU

It's never more pronounced than when I've been drinking. The thoughts and memories of you are burned into my soul. Your laughter, voice, touch, and smell are all still very present. We've not lived together for months. Our divorce has been final for almost a month, just shy of our fourth anniversary. I feel this deep emptiness. I'm fascinated that we still feel these things despite having moved on. To have gone from love, laughter, and commitment, to longing, emptiness, sorrow, and sadness. I will be forever amazed at how we invite people into our lives with the hope that they will be there forever, the belief that they will be, only to one day find them gone. I've been fine for a while. I find my thoughts and my heart yearning for another. There are rare days when you are still here and very present within me. I remember the kisses, hugs, joys, and sorrows. Days like today sneak up and steal the focus of what is to insert what was. Oh, the mixed joy and sorrow, these remnants of you.

THE PHOENIX

It all came crashing down. Suddenly. Unexpectedly. The hurt, the pain, the damage caused by the wreckage was devastating. How would I survive? It was all gone. Everything. The life, the love, the laughter, the joy. However, as the flames continued to burn and time crept in, it changed. The fire burnt lower. The flame went from apparent red-orange to a barely visible blue. It burned hotter. The embers glowed. From the decimation, something stirred. From the destruction, something could and would be born. It wasn't the end; it was a transformation. From the ashes of what was, something new would emerge. The embers moved, ever so slightly. New life, new energy was being born of the ashes—a Phoenix. When it is ready, that Phoenix will rise from the ashes, spread its fiery wings, and look at each with awe and wonder. It will consume everything when it rises; the flame will burn bright and light a new path. The Phoenix is coming.

II

PART TWO

She Who Touched my Mind (My Rebirth)

RENEWAL

A new day dawns as the sun does rise.

Darkness flees, and light pierces the skies.

The somber scenery fades away.

It cannot compete with the radiant rays.

The sullenness that accompanied the night

Is all but vanquished with the coming of the light.

The mood has changed since the darkness waned.

A smile permeates her lips as amber waves reign.

SMILE

In a picture, I see it.

In her voice, I hear it.

It brightens a room.

When she speaks, I can hear when it appears as relaxation becomes evident, and her tone changes.

Her soft, sensual voice then transitions to playful embarrassment, followed by a burst of giddy laughter that soothes and elicits comfort and joy.

The change is seamless, almost effortless, when she puts it on her face.

Now, her beaming presence is seen without me trying.

It radiates, lighting up a room, a phone conversation, even a chat session.

It communicates joy, happiness, and possibility. It is magic.

Her smile.

FIRST ENCOUNTER

She called him as she parked in the hotel parking lot. He had been waiting for her to arrive; he did not allow anything but calm excitement to course through him. Her voice was as soft, sweet, and soothing as he had come to know it, making him smile. They were meeting for the first time after weeks of conversation. Everything had been unfolding like a song building. They had mutually decided to meet halfway between their homes.

He greeted her call with the same fluctuating intonation she had come to know. She thought his voice was sexy. She didn't hesitate to tell him that she loved hearing his voice, that she couldn't wait to see him with her own eyes. He sauntered down the stairs toward the lobby. She had parked in the back lot. The conversation flowed like it always had, natural and unforced.

As he walked out of the hotel, he smiled. He hung up the phone as he laid his eyes on the woman the first time. She smiled back. She approached with a purpose—to embrace him. They wrapped their arms around each other, taking in each other's scents, maintaining their composure despite their mutual excitement. Hearts were pounding; they were memorizing each other through touch.

As they pulled apart, they gazed at each other. The woman's green eyes pierced him, and his blue eyes her. Her smile commanded the sun to diminish its radiance.

He announced, "I'm going to kiss you now."

"Okay," she responded excitedly.

Their lips touched—softly at first, then transforming into a deepening kiss, until their tongues danced together. It was as if they had already known each other. The woman sighed, and it was music to the man's ears. He lightly nibbled the bottom of her lips. Time stood still. It was breathtaking for them both.

After what was surely an eternity, they slowly, reluctantly pulled their lips apart; they smiled, sighed, and laughed.

"I've been thinking about that all week," he said, staring into her beautiful eyes as she beamed.

"I have, too," she responded, "and it was wonderful."

BECOMING ONE

They lay there, bare, drinking each other in with their eyes. He looked at her, intoxicated by her presence. She bit her lip as she stared at him. He thought she was sexy, and she, him. They both were enraptured by the intelligence of the other. She seemed timid at his sculpted, mature body while being self-conscious of her self-described "mom body." He thought her intelligence and emotional nature added to her natural beauty, which made her extremely attractive—and hoped she believed how much. Their eyes mapped Each other's naked bodies, causing his mouth to water as he imagined the moments ahead while her eyes widened as she took him in with her stare.

They kissed as softly as the first time they had kissed. He nibbled her lip and mapped her body with his fingertips. He could feel her tremble at his touch, distracting him as he caressed her.

She lay down on the soft bed while he continued to kiss her. Gently, he used his mouth to map her body. From her cheeks to her inner thighs, he explored her. She held her breath. Sensitive to how she was feeling, he asked if she was okay. She nodded, biting her lip.

He kissed his way up her thighs, gradually approaching her apex. He breathed across her clit. She moaned, her arousal apparent at the ease with which his index and middle fingers entered her. His mouth watered as his fingers entered her gently. She arched her back and cried out as he moved his fingers inside her.

He continued moving ever closer until his lips wrapped themselves around her clitoris. He dragged his tongue across her hood, fingers still moving. He did not rush as he savored the taste of her; his mouth watered. She continued to exhibit signs of extreme pleasure. Occasionally, he nibbled on her inner thighs, licked her folds, and lightly blew cool air over her.

As she reached a crescendo, she pushed his face from her body, struggling to breathe. He wiped her from his lips and chin as he climbed between her legs. She was biting her lip. Her eyes pierced him with desire. She reached down and grabbed his cock, guiding him into her. She tilted her head back as he entered her. They kissed. She trembled as she welcomed him inside and sighed as their abdomens met.

She wrapped her legs and arms around him as they kissed passionately. They moved in unison. Slowly. Methodically. He stared into her eyes, gyrating against her, taking in her lip biting. They clasped hands, locked lips, and thrust in counterpoint together.

They stared into each other's eyes, deep into each other's souls, as their pleasure crested. They were one.

WILD RIDE

So close and so far away. My mind wanders, thinks of the smiles while also faintly feeling worried or concerned. That connection. That comfort of feeling so connected to someone. It is such a fantastic feeling. To feel appreciated for my intelligence and humor, for the way I view the world and approach things. To feel her touch, even when she is not near me, and to crave her, makes me hungry. Hungry for her presence. Will it work? I believe it can, but, like anything, it will take time. There are so many things that need to happen. My attention and focus are pulled in so many different directions. It will be easy to dream and not do. I want to do. I want to do so many things, and go to so many places with her. It is wonderful to feel special, and I hope she does, too. It may just be the best thing yet on this wild ride of life.

III

PART THREE

She Who Touched my Soul (My Wave)

SINGLE ROSE

A single rose, so well defined.
Its rival in beauty is so hard to find.
But it just might take a dozen, or two,
To rival the beauty I find in you.

IF YOU

In the event our respective sleep prevents us from Chatting, or talking or enjoying the company of each other, let me leave you with this:

If you must hurt, do so from caring and hoping.

If you are weak, be so from exerting so much strength.

If you need a smile, know someone is thinking about you.

If you are exhausted, believe it was from a day on the swings, laughing.

When you drift into slumber, hope for the strength to hang on to the swings while laughing with that someone.

That someone is me.

SEE

If you are the sun, I want to see you rise.

If you are a flower, I want to see you bloom.

If you are the moon, I want to see you bright and full.

If you are anything, I want to see you.

TEMPESTUOUS SOUL

You are a tempestuous soul whose depth rivals that of Challenger Deep.

Your smile lights up a room, and your laugh rivals a choir of angels.

I cannot wait to see you again.

It feels like several eternities until then, despite knowing it's soon.

EXQUISITE

At last, they were alone. Another amazing night, despite the torrential downpour that had soaked them earlier. The movie they had seen allowed them to share many things. Popcorn. Laughter. Glances. Hands, intertwined. They had eaten a late dinner, and she asked him if he minded taking her to pick up a few things for her family's Thanksgiving meal. He didn't mind. It was more time and attentiveness. It led back to this moment. She was nervous, despite Them having been with each other the previous night. A past trauma wreaked havoc on the normal biological responses she felt when with him. Her heart raced, her face blushed, and she glanced up to meet the kind blue eyes gazing at her as if she were the first sunrise the world had seen. Having something to drink often helped take the edge off. She hadn't had any. He placed his lips softly upon hers and caressed her jawline. She trembled as butterflies swelled within him.

"I'm so nervous," she said.

"How about we start with my lips exploring your body like last night. We don't have to do anything else," he said to her.

"Mmmm, I do love your kisses," she responded, biting her lip.

He gently took her hands, and they strolled to her bedroom. She lay upon the bed. He climbed next to her and again lost his breathe in the softness of her lips. After a few minutes, he stood and began to remove his clothing.

"I'm removing my shirt and pants to prevent me from overheating," he began with a laugh. "The rest remains on unless you say otherwise."

He was sensitive to her anxiety because of what he knew of her past. She seemed to appreciate his concern for her. He climbed back onto the bed and looked at her. Her top was sleeveless. He took her right hand, gently, and lifted her palm to his lips. Kiss. Her wrist. Kiss. Her forearm, where her tribute tattoo to her mother was. Kiss. Her upper arm and shoulder. Kiss. Her neck. Nibble. Kiss. Her jawline. Kiss. Again, her lips, as if to resuscitate a woman who had ceased breathing. Their mouths danced, his tongue stealing away moments with her tongue and top lip. He pulled away briefly to gaze at her. She bit her lip, staring back. Her left side needed the same attention, and he obliged her.

"May I remove your top?" he asked.

"Yes."

More to kiss. Each side of her neck. Panting. Kiss. Each shoulder. Kiss. Each clavicle. Kiss. Between her covered breasts. Kiss. Her stomach and each side. Kiss.

He placed his index fingers within the waist of her pants, "May I remove these?"

"Yes."

He gazed upon her body and smiled. "You're so sexy."

"Thank you, but I'm not."

His eyes told her a different story; he hoped she read it. Then, her hips and thighs. Kiss. Her knees. Kiss. Calves. Kiss. He continued, occasionally re-tracing his steps to remind her body of his lips.

"Your ladies are missing out; may I remove your bra?"

"Yes," she said with a sigh, chuckling at the term ladies.

He tasted her lips again, their tongues dancing slowly. He moved slowly towards her breasts, kissing around and underneath them, while also breathing heavily upon them. Her right nipple felt his warm tongue reach out to her, and she quivered and sighed. His teeth gently nibbled, and he blew softly upon it. Her left nipple couldn't be missed, so he made his way over.

He lay next to her and spent time kissing, licking, breathing, caressing. No rush. Time and attentiveness. Hours passed.

"Is this okay?" he asked, as he placed his hand over her panties.

"Yes."

"May I remove them?"

"Yes."

He removed her panties, and again he lay next to her. Kiss. Kiss.

"Shall I remove mine?"

"No."

He didn't. He kissed her lips, caressed her skin, and retraced his steps with his lips. Shoulders. Arms. Breasts. Stomach. Hips. Thighs. He placed his right middle finger just above her clitoris.

"May I?"

"Yes," she panted.

He kissed her again as his hand gently caressed her labia. Wetness coated his finger as it entered her.

"Do you want me inside of you?"

"Yes."

"Shall I remove these?" he asked, placing her right hand upon his underwear.

"Yes."

He stood to remove his underwear and then knelt upon the bed. He spoke her name and told her how beautiful and sexy she was.

"I am going to put this under you," he said, as he grasped at one of the pillows and placed it under her hips to elevate her.

He climbed between her legs and proceeded to kiss her lips, neck, and breasts. He slowly inserted himself into her.

"I am so wet," she said to him.

"Yes, you are. It's making me harder."

"Oh, yes. I can feel it. That's hot."

As before, there was no rushing. Like strokes of a brush touching a canvas, beauty would be painted. He pushed into her, kissing, thrusting, and rubbing up against her. Their bodies tangled as he slowly deepened his presence and drew back. Kiss.

"You are so wet."

"I am from all the kissing. Faster, I'm so close."

He thrust deeply and shifted gears. Thrust, thrust, thrust. Thrust, thrust, thrust. Kiss. She sighed, and tension was released. They had to be quiet, with sleeping teens just doors away. He looked at her, and he began to pulse, uncontrollably. With a final thrust, he gasped, as his orgasm followed hers. His warm presence caused her to gasp. Kiss. Kiss. Kiss.

They settled into bed, and he wrapped his arm Around her as her big, safe spoon. Her back and shoulder exposed to those tantalizing lips of his. Back. Kiss. Neck. Kiss. Shoulder. Kiss.

"I hope you sleep well and have pleasant dreams," he said, kissing her neck and shoulder again.

"I will. I hope you do, too," she responded softly, enjoying being wrapped up in him.

They slept.

LAUGH

She giggled as she told him the story of the nickname her dad had given her. She expressed embarrassment over the name, but he could hear the smile and imagine the blush on her face as she recalled something so personal and fond; his smile, unseen but as wide as the sky, was a reflection of what she must have been feeling.

"I love your laugh," he said, unable to withhold the simple truth of the statement.

"Why?" she asked, coyly, the blush again apparent.

He knew of three laughs of hers. The giggle was a laugh that might start from a place of nervousness or shyness, but was endearing in its cuteness. The chuckle was a soft laugh that would slip past any attempt to suppress it. Finally—the laugh that could best be described as an unbridled laugh, an out-loud laugh. A roar that was so contagious those around her would fall victim to that which had no cure. He loved them all. From the shy, reserved blush that came with most of them to the one that showed how much joy she had within her. All of them were heavenly. His ears rejoiced at the sound as if he were attending an angelic choir.

"I think it is wonderful, and I can hear you blushing. There are not sufficient words I can say right now that can properly convey what I love about your laugh. I'll have to think of words that may be able to do it justice," he answered.

She chuckled, and he smiled and knew. Her laugh, quite simply, was perfect.

BLISS

He lay there, staring at her while she slept. She had just rolled to her back and turned her head slightly to the left. She had draped her left leg over his right and drawn her hands up to her chin. He smiled. She looked so calm. Comfortable. Beautiful. She wouldn't think of being called beautiful, so early in the day, but he believed it. She was at peace. He placed his hand on her inner thigh while her leg rested on him. Her soft lips slightly parted as she forced air through them. A cute snore. He couldn't remove his gaze from her. He wondered if she was dreaming and, if so, what danced before her mind's eye.

Her body was so close to him, her leg still draped, her shoulder touching his. It was as if she was aware of him and longed to be close even as she slept soundly. He reveled in her scent as his lips approached her shoulder again. He continued to smile while taking moments to kiss her shoulder softly. Kiss. His lips lingered on her soft skin.

The morning progressed. Breathing. Leg draping. Shoulder kissing. Smiling. He wished he could have a permanent picture of the moment, but the memory would have to suffice. She woke. Her eyes opened slowly and as she focused she caught his gaze. A smile appeared, vanished, and appeared again. She softly hummed. He returned the smile, leaned over, and kissed her soft lips. She smiled again. It was bliss.

WILD THINGS

A depth not seen, unless one looks,
Beyond a smiling face.
It is there, in her soul;
Wild things in that place.

DO YOU KNOW?

Do you know how amazing you are?
To be chased because of what people see
Is something that genuinely saddens me.
For, in your eyes, I see the depths of your soul.
It is there that, slowly, we must fill a hole
Caused by a life with abused loyalty and trust.
Surround yourself with goodness—you must.
Do you know how beautiful your laugh is to me?
Can you imagine colored leaves on a tree
Or the music played by the waves of the sea?
Those are some things I can see
When I hear the music of your laughter ring in my ear.
Do you know how your thoughts turn me on?
I listen intently, mourning your words when they're gone.
Waiting for more, making me fawn.
Do you know how your kiss makes me feel?
Soft, gentle lips; the bliss is for real.
Let it never end; let our souls seal.
Do you know how your blush gives you away?

When kind words come, you keep them at bay.
The kindness I give, you deserve, I do say.
Do you know how much you mean?
Not just to kids, animals, or family, you see,
But also to someone who sees your soul. Me.

SATISFY

If I were there with you right now, do you know what I would do to you? I would tear your clothes off of you and throw them behind me, uncaring, my eyes affixed to your supple tits. The hunger in my eyes would tell you what I want to do. I would remove my clothes quickly because I could not wait to fuck you. You'd be biting your lips, waiting for me. I would remove my pants, and you would see what you have done to my cock. I'd be ready for you. I would push you down onto the bed, and your nipples would become the focus of my teeth. Your hips clasped in my hands. I would roll you to the side, smack your sexy ass and bite it. Damn, you are so sexy.

I would spread your legs and slowly insert my hard cock into you. Slowly at first. Grinding. You are getting wetter. That is so fucking hot. Do you feel me getting harder? You do that to me. Your sounds ignite me. You are making me harder. Fucking you harder and faster. You grip the sheets at first, and then you grasp my ass, pulling me into you. You're so fucking sexy. You come. The sounds and faces you make are ecstasies. I come next. Feel me inside you? Pulsing. Warm. I love to satisfy you.

CLOSE

After they had moved with each other and finished being joined together, they cuddled close as they always had done. Her right leg was draped over him, his right hand gently rubbing the soft skin of her thigh. Their breathing was slowing, as were their hearts. Her sounds, just minutes before, had ignited his entire being. She loved the culmination of his affections while inside of her.

They talked, as they often did, about anything. Laughing. Smiling. Touching. He brushed her hair behind her ear, kissed her forehead, nose, and lips. She rolled over to her side, to take the little spoon position. He snuggled closer, sliding his arm under her pillow, as his other hand began caressing her thigh, hip, and ass. She felt calm and slipped into a gentle slumber. He soon followed.

His brain became energized as he entered a dream state. Dreams abounded during the soothing slumber next to her—first, a nightmare. One so startling, he awoke, heart racing. He occasionally had those and worked to calm himself. He looked over and smiled as he heard her soft, gentle breathing. Sleep soon again found him.

This time, slumber had taken him to a pleasant dream with her. The backdrop was a candlelit room with the aroma of cinnamon and apple, her favorites. She was lying on the bed, beckoning to him with her eyes; body exposed. She could see the hunger in his eyes as he removed his shirt and pants, revealing his tight boxer briefs. She bit her lip as she drank in his form. He removed his undershorts and exposed his engorged cock—the result of seeing her there.

He climbed into bed and slowly made his way on top of her. Lips locking. Tongues dancing. Goosebumps forming. He kissed her cheeks, nibbled her neck and collar bones. Eventually, her nipples knew the softness of his lips, anticipated his bite, and the wetness of his tongue. Her body responded to his touch, preparing for him to be inside of her. She was ready as soon as he'd nibbled her nipples.

She grabbed his cock, gently, and guided it into her. Their eyes met as they were both bathed in the ecstasy of becoming one. She was ready for him, and she made him harder. They made music with their bodies.

Suddenly, he woke. He saw her there, sleeping. He was hard and craved her. He pulled her near, caressing her ass and thigh. Kissing, nibbling. Nibbling, kissing. She woke and looked at him.

"I want you," he said, in that voice she loved.

She smiled as she adjusted to lie on her back, reaching to pull him near. He climbed between her legs.

He woke. Startled, he looked around, reaching to the other side of the bed to pull her close. He was at home, in his bed, alone. He turned the other pillow sideways, rolled over, and pulled it close. He thought of her.

MAKE LOVE TO YOUR HEART

On a day when you cannot climb out of bed
Because of the pain from your illness or ache in your head,
I want you to know that I still see you there, the
same as before.
I do not love you less; I love you more.
In you, I see the fear of intimacy,
And it often causes you to push at me.
When you do, are you asking *why?*
Why is he here with me, like this, this guy?
There are good days and bad. The yin and the yang.
Days full of laughter, while others with pain.
On days where you want me inside you, up close,
But you tell me we can't, the pain's at its most.
Do not fret there, my sweet; I'll hold you tight, and impart:
When that occurs, I'll make love to your heart.

CONNECTION

To some, a connection makes sense. It is something that resonates deeply with a lot of people. For others, context is necessary. I'm thankful my mom asks questions to understand things better. In talking with her about the grief that I was feeling, I explained that it was due to the profound emotional connection I had with a woman. I told her of the last time I felt this way, twenty-three years ago, and how, when I felt it again recently, it awakened a part of me I had long since forgotten. I felt like parts of me were on fire. It was all-consuming. Thoughts. Feelings. Touch. Sight. Sound. Everything. To sense her without touching her was the most challenging thing to try to explain. But bless my mom; she listened.

I finally managed to express it in a way she understood. I told her that my ex-wife was the only person I ever wanted to marry and that despite that feeling and how much I loved her, I had never felt like this. This feeling was a deep, profound connection to another soul. A couple of tears fell from my eyes as my mom came in to hug me.

"Wow! I had no idea that's how it felt for you," she said, as she embraced me. "I love you."

I could feel her, even when she wasn't present. When we were together, what she said, when she said nothing, spoke volumes.

It was a connection.

LOVE HURTS

All I want to do is kiss you until we are dizzy; until time melts away into oblivion. To express my love and passion without words is the most profound way I can communicate how I feel about you. Oh, how I long for you to let go of fear and to lose yourself in that idyllic place to which we transport ourselves when our lips touch. That fear hurts my soul.

To make love with you is an extension of two souls bonding, staring into each other's eyes, biting our lips, smiling, and kissing. We go slow, so the pain from your interstitial cystitis is reduced and does not linger when we want passion and sexual energy to consume us. There is an ache in my heart, knowing that our very expressions of caring for one another cause pain. It is because I love you that I do not wish to hurt you. How do I love you, when love hurts?

IV

PART FOUR

She Came Crashing Down

PUSH AND PULL

Push and pull like waves in the sea.
Push and pull like gravity.
Push like a shove—a hefty one, too.
Then a pull, bringing me back to you.
Pull me close, for a warm, gentle kiss.
Push me back, afraid of the bliss.
Pull when calm, wanting to feel.
Push again, when it feels too real.
Push and pull, like tides on the shore.
Push and pull, wanting less, wanting more.
Push me away because of the fear.
Pull me close, craving me near.
Pull on me, trapped in that gaze.
Push on me, dazed by the haze.
Pull so near, for my strong, safe embrace.
Push again, keeping safe your dark place.
Push and pull, is this an urge?
Push and pull, are you trying to purge?
Pull me in: with your eyes, laugh, and smile.
Push me out; I'll die for a while.

NOT ENOUGH

To give your all and still fall short,
Is not something that matters in work or sport.
But in pursuit of something more?
Something for which there is no score?
To court someone, to date, or love,
A special someone you're always thinking of.
To pour your all, mind, heart, and soul
Into actions and words, and be left with a hole.
It is deep in the heart, where this pain is felt,
Wounded and hurting, from the blow that's been dealt.
I gave everything I had and was told I'm too good.
It ended too soon, I did all that I could.
I tried anew, with a soulmate this time,
The feelings with her were downright sublime.
Unfortunately, it ends, this time in rebuff,
And I'm left empty, my best not enough.

DYING

He sat there at their Christmas party, surrounded by friends with whom he sweated in daily workouts. Surrounded, yet alone. His soul yearned for hers. So far away, no contact but deeply connected. Tears beckoned, but he held them back. Her smile burned into his memory. It haunted him as he heard the chattering in the background. The laughter, fellowship, friendship, allowed a fake smile to creep onto his face, but the hole in his heart consumed him. What was she doing? He wished she wanted him as much as he wanted her. He ached for her. Her voice, her laugh, her smile. He was haunted by her intrinsic beauty when he closed his eyes. If only he could kiss her. If only she wanted his kiss. He ached, and it was his soul dying.

LOSS

He missed her. It had been a couple of days since they had seen each other. He felt as though she was no longer interested in the best parts of him. How could they operate? How could it work if emptiness was what she sought? He had been here before. He needed all of himself unified. What she had asked was not something he was unwilling to do, but he needed it to come from a different place.

He missed the little things about her. Her laugh. Her voice. Her smile. Her touch. Her kiss. Cuddling her and kissing her shoulder. The occasions she was too tired to climb out of bed were something he enjoyed, despite knowing how much her physical pain hindered her.

She had indicated earlier that she didn't want to rush it. He was happy to oblige her, as he didn't want to rush either. However, she often brought up the concept of relationships; she was eager to label theirs something more physical and less emotional. That hurt his heart. They didn't need to rush. He would have preferred "not interested", or anything else that would have communicated that she didn't want him to continue pursuing her. However, now they had this label that conveyed sex was okay, but feelings were unwelcome.

Traveling six hundred miles to see her was worth the treasure of the little things he loved about her. However, now he questioned how to proceed because his "only" reason to go now was not enough. He felt a great loss. He missed the woman he had fallen for. Was she still there? Had she ever been?

MOMENT

Let this be a tragic story of two people at different times and places, never having their moment to shine as one. I cannot chase or convince, because then it would be more about me than you or us. I want to stretch out my hand, to say *I like you and I'd like to get to know you better.* For the first time in a long time, if ever, I have felt more than what others around me are feeling. I know with certainty the feelings are mine, and not another's. To not feel someone else's anxiety, pain, joy, or sorrow, but my profundity of passion, excitement, anxiety, fear, pain, and comfort. I cannot chase that which does not want to be caught. It would kill me.

WILL YOU?

Without building it, the connection will fade.
Will you miss it one day?
Conversations, laughter, bathing in the sounds of
each other's voices.
Will you miss them after these choices?
Kissing, touching, intertwining our bodies and souls.
Will you feel a tremendous hole?
When you utter my name in any place,
Will you smile fondly, and think of my smiling face?
While you lie there in bed, craving a touch,
Will you remember me, caressing your butt?
When you wake in the morning and open your eyes,
Will you miss my gaze, as blue as the sky?
When you have a day overcome with anxiety and fear,
Will you miss my arms pulling you near?
When you are overwhelmed with the world and its
noise,
Will you miss the soothing sound of my voice?

When you have thoughts and are longing to be heard,
Will you miss me taking in every uttered word?
I will honor your wishes and bid you adieu.
I will ache with longing. Will you?

WAS THAT YOU?

They say that when you dream of someone, they are thinking about you, but perhaps I was just thinking of you. However, the sentiment is sweet. To imagine you were thinking what I was dreaming. The last moment we spent in your bed, intertwined, gazing into each other's eyes. Kissing, smiling, and being taken into you in more than one way. Touching each other.

When you speak of intimacy issues, do you secretly harbor a longing for intimacy? I could see the vulnerability in your eyes. The surrender. The invitation. When I woke, it took a few moments to recall where I was. My body attuned to the dream, memory, or thought of you. Were you thinking of me, dreaming of me? I could feel our hands clasped together, your lips with mine, and your breath with mine, your gyrations synced to mine. I could feel you squeezing me. Was that you, planting that unforgettable dream in my head?

INDELIBLE

Your soft voice, infectious laugh, radiant smile, sultry eyes, hypnotic scent, everything is missed. My mind, body, heart, and soul yearn for your thoughts, touch, love, and presence. Utterly so. I wish to gaze into your beautiful eyes, which expose the depth of your being. It is there that your vulnerability is hidden away from others. You cannot hide it from me. I see it, I feel it, and I smile.

Oh, to taste your lips again would be heaven. My fingertips miss tracing your body. They connected your sporadic and light freckles like constellations in the night sky with imaginary lines. I miss keeping you close and warm while caressing your arm and kissing your shoulder. All these memories replay in my mind. I miss breathing you in deeply, closing my eyes and reveling in the ecstasy I derive from you. My mind ignites with the memories of our conversations, your thoughts, and how you articulate them.

I miss you. I want to get lost in the memories. I want to close my eyes and never wake from these dreams and memories, but alas, I am here without you. These memories of you I will always keep. Will you keep yours of me? Will you meet me in my dreams and memories? I will save a spot for you. You've left an indelible mark on my soul.

PRECIOUS STONE

To my precious stone,
The emerald of my life.
You with the ruby right,
Whom I wish was near at night.
My inner romantic wishes you were here with me.
My solemn realist knows it will never be.
May you radiate that blue-white light.
For, in another life, I'm holding you tight.

V

PART FIVE

Transformation

PIECES

Like a porcelain figurine, he stood. His heart adorned on his sleeve while hers resided in his chest. Like so many others before her, she had parts of her heart within him. A patchwork of each unique soul glued together to form this man.

Her words were blunt, brutal, and cutting, each one cracking the porcelain. His smile held while tears streamed down his face. His torso began to crack. Words. Cracks. Cracks. Words. Was she trying to break him? Could she not see through the smile? Could she not see the tears? Could she not see the cracks? Word after word, crack after crack, the rift grew. He knew what he needed to do, but his heart felt something else. He reached his sleeve and removed his heart. He extended it out to her while continuing to smile through the tears. He could not see her face. The words blinded his soul, and the tears blurred his vision.

More words. Crushing. She swiped at his offering. His heart fell to the floor. Time slowed. Each beat of the falling heart echoed.

Bump, bump. Bump, bump.

It shattered on contact, and with the last round of harsh words, the final crack in the porcelain man was his undoing. He exploded and fell to the floor with the shards of his heart. Hers was still in his chest.

He lay there, fragmented, her memory in the not-too-distant past. He knew he must continue. How?

"Continue," he said to himself.

"How?"

"While you will never be the same, you will be whole."

At that, each fragment drew closer to one another, the sound of glass scraping across the floor echoing. As if yearning to be connected, each joined with another, and another, and another. Over time, the porcelain developed a whole, unique man, with mended but visible cracks. He was not like he was before; his heart was missing from his sleeve.

"I am not the same."

"No, but you are whole."

"Why am I not the same?"

"You cannot be the same. Somebody broke you. Your parts mixed with her parts and all the other parts before her. You have healed. You are whole. You are now a complete person with all the other fragments. They are a part of you. Forever. It is up to you to decide how to proceed."

"I can still love?"

"If you wish."

"I can abstain?"

"If you wish."

"What if that happens again?"

"It may, and it will hurt just the same, maybe more. However, you will be whole again if you choose."

"But I will be different?"

"To some degree, but only because of the pieces. They will be different."

"Then I choose to love again."

"That is wise."

He smiled, and his heart appeared on his sleeve again, but it was different. It was bigger than before. It had more pieces.

RADIANT

He stared into the dark place; a shudder coursed through him. He had been there before and could sense the woman's presence and anguish. He could hear her but saw nothing. He closed his eyes to see with his soul. There she was, cowered in the darkness, tears pouring from her eyes.

He reached out and whispered, "Take my hand."

She recoiled; her fear from where she had come consumed her. Her light was dim.

"Take my hand," he whispered again.

He stepped closer to the dark place. The woman turned toward the wall, fearing the outstretched hand and gentle voice. He was going to have to show her before her light went out. His hands came together in a cradle at his chest, eyes closed so he could continue to see her with his soul.

Cracks appeared across his torso—scars from his encounters with the darkness. A blue-white light radiated from within him. A tear crawled from his eye and gently kissed his cheek before softly splashing on the ground. A stream of tears followed as he fell to one knee, pain apparent on his face. The light began to flow outward from the tears that bathed the ground.

She looked toward him, and for a moment, the fear subsided. With the light, he could see her cracks and scars, the darkness weaving in and out of them.

He fell to both knees, radiating everything he could muster. His cracks and scars were burning bright. A faint twinkle appeared in her eyes.

"See. I'm like you. You don't have to let it consume you."

She slowly crawled toward him. A shriek cried out from the dark place. She paused, paralyzed by fear.

"It's okay," he whispered.

She continued forward into his open arms.

"You are broken but beautiful. You are stronger than what broke you."

She cried uncontrollably, tears of relief. He caressed her hair and gently kissed her forehead. His tears fell upon her scars, and her pain subsided. He looked in her eyes, and while he traced her scars with his fingertips, he smiled.

"These will remain. The memories of how you got them will haunt you, but your light can burn as bright as before. We may be broken, but we are beautiful."

She smiled, and it was radiant.

ANGUISH

It had been some time since she had escaped the dark place. Her cracks and scars set, and her healing was slow. He spent time exposing her to the radiance with which she was trying to reconnect. There were days of progress, laughter, light, and radiant beauty. Then, there would be setbacks.

She lay there, eyes slowly opening to catch his kind gaze, while he brushed her hair behind her right ear. A faint smile appeared on her face. He returned the smile.

"You seem rested," he started softly, with a voice she had grown to love. "Let's try again."

"Okay," she responded softly.

She sat up and turned to face him as he adjusted to meet her, crossing his legs. He placed his wrists on his knees, palms up.

"Place your hands on mine," he said.

She slowly placed her hands on his, palms down. He smiled, and his blue eyes communicated a kindness she had never experienced before. She could feel the energy rising from within him. His cracks and scars began to glow with the bluish-white light she had grown accustomed to seeing radiate from him. She loved how he could light up a room. She could feel him.

"Now you try," he instructed calmly.

She closed her eyes to concentrate. A dim light began to radiate from her cracks and scars. Their eyes met as they smiled and shared their light and energy. They laughed, their skin sensitive to the heat. Suddenly, a slight wince appeared on her face.

"Focus. Let it flow. Be here. Be present," he said, as he felt pain well up inside her.

"I can't. I can't," she replied with tears as her light flickered. In her mind's eye, memories of her time in the dark place began to cycle through her mind. She closed her eyes as the painful memories came to the fore.

"Concentrate," he reminded, as he attempted to absorb the pain from her.

Her tears streamed uncontrollably, as the pain became the overriding feeling. Her soul began to scream. He could hear her psyche call out in anguish, but his ears only heard the sobbing. As the pain increased, her eyes shot open, and the scream from deep within her soul found its voice in hers. Her light flickered out. The scream shattered the glasses and windows of the room. The hairs on his body stood as he attempted to wrap her in his comforting light.

Another scream welled up in her soul and found its way out. The force was so great that it pushed him from where he sat. He flew backward, arms and legs flailing, careening toward the wall, as his own light faded. He met the wall across the room with a thud, wind escaping his chest with urgency, his head striking the wall with concussive force. He fell to the ground, unmoving as she sat, crying. The screams stopped. Torn between want and fear, she wanted the light, but the pain and fear caused her to push him away.

He stirred slowly.

"We'll try again soon," he began weakly. "But first, some rest."

He collapsed into sleep, while she cried with fading recollections of anguish.

RESCUE

He was startled awake as she tensely wiggled next to him. She must have been having another nightmare. Her breathing was labored, and her hands gripped the sheet near her chin. He reached across her with his left hand to brush her hair away from her eyes. He could feel her fear.

She rolled to her right side, whimpering. He spooned her, draped his arm over her, and let his blue-white light shine as he entered slumber with her. He opened his eyes and was kneeling in a home surrounded by a foreboding, remote forest. Only mirrors throughout; there were no furnishings.

From the other room, he heard her scream. He stood quickly and ran to the door separating them. It felt cold. He could feel pain and fear. He gripped the knob, the brass cold in his hand, but it was locked. He stepped back, his body wrapped in his light, while his eyes began to glow with a small red flame. Blue-gray armor encased him as he kicked at the door with his right leg. The door flew open.

He walked through the doorway. Throughout the room, circling near the ceiling, were dark smoky entities. In the corner furthest from him, she cowered. A shadowy figure imposingly stood over her, and the darkness was seeping into her cracks and scars.

"You can beat him," he shouted across the room. The dark entities screeched in unison; she covered her ears.

"Your pain is your fuel for the fire. Use it. Remember what I taught you."

She looked at him, then at the dark figure reaching for her. Her eyes began to glow with the same red flame as the blue-white light began to radiate. She punched the mysterious figure in the throat, and it collapsed to one knee. The figure outstretched its right arm. She gripped its wrist, twisted it, and delivered a devastating strike, shattering its arm. At this, the other entities began to descend from their orbit near the ceiling. The dark skies outside seemed to feed them.

He managed to form a sword and ran towards her, swinging and striking down the darkness. Two entities approached him and pushed him up against a wall containing a large wall mirror. Their reflections formed two more bodies that groped at him through the looking glass, gripping his arms and forcing the sword from his hand. Concern became evident on his face.

She looked and saw him struggling, but remained focused on her demon. Others approached her. She glanced across the room to see the four entities take her knight of light into the looking glass, while the remaining beings turned toward her. The darkness smiled eerily.

"You're mine now," it whispered.

She screamed—not from pain, or fear, but of determination. Emerald armor surrounded her; her right arm affixed with a harness holding a blade, with a ruby hilt. Her left arm held a small-caliber machine gun. She stared the darkness in the sockets where eyes would be.

"You're done here," she said as she jammed the blade deep into the chest cavity of the darkness.

She fired the machine gun, taking precision aim at the other entities. Their shrieks were startling as they fell and vanished.

"Nooo! You're mine," yelled the darkness.

"No. I belong to me," she responded confidently, as she twisted the blade.

The darkness shrieked before it vanished. The remaining entities fell one by one until none remained. The woman gathered her thoughts, and then hurried to the mirror. She peered into it and saw him lying against the wall, with a darkness kneeling over him, his light faint. She looked behind her, but he was not there. He was in the mirror.

His eyes looked up at the woman kneeling over him, against a backdrop of trees and a waterfall. She smiled at him while his eyes filled with a combination of joy, pain, and confusion. The kneeling woman placed her hand on his chest. He winced.

From outside the mirror, she saw the dark, kneeling figure reach into his chest and grip his heart. She could see him wince, light flickering, as the dark form appeared to kiss him, and consume his light.

"No!" she yelled and pounded on the mirror, looking for a way to get to him.

The man felt the kneeling woman kiss him, and he became overcome with weakness. He remembered her face as tears formed.

"Why? How are you here?" he asked, being only met with a smile.

From outside the mirror, she cried watching his light diminish. Then, she looked up, placed both hands on the mirror, and her weapons and armor vanished. Her radiance began to shine brighter than ever before. With a bright flash, she appeared inside the mirror. To her, it was a dark, dilapidated version of the room from which she came.

"Dammit," she began, shouting his name. "Remember, our pain is the fuel of our fire, but it's your heart that ignites the flame. You are the kindest man I've ever known, and even though I'm not ready, I cannot imagine a world without your heart."

He opened his eyes, and the façade of trees, waterfall, and beautiful familiar landscape transformed into a dark room in disrepair, with a shadowy figure gripping and ripping at his heart. The foreboding creature began to drain his light with a kiss.

"Remember! Please!" he heard from across the room, from the radiant beauty he had come to know.

Memories flooded him. Laughter. Dinners. Soft touches. Kisses. Her smile when receiving flowers. Their bodies intertwined. His heart began to burn and beat vigorously, his eyes on fire, his blue-white light glowing. The dark figure shrieked as it released the grip on his heart, in apparent pain from being singed.

The memories shared by him and the radiant beauty played repeatedly in his mind as he placed his left hand over his heart and his right hand gripped the head of the darkness. A flame burst from his hand, and the gloom dissolved. His fire and light dissipated but did not disappear.

She rushed over to him, and he could feel her connection as she touched him. She leaned in to kiss him, and they woke. He was lying on his back, her lips pressed against his. They looked in each other's eyes, smiling. Glowing.

"When we began this journey," he began, "I never imagined that the pieces of me I had long forgotten would ever return. After all this time, it was me who needed rescuing."

She smiled, and said softly, "Even the strongest of us need rescuing, from time to time."

THE GIFT

They were together, bodies joined and inter-twined. Each was radiating their own light from their cracks and scars. They would stare deeply into each other's souls one moment, and the next close their eyes to feel the energy between them. They would again exchange gazes and then kiss. Softly. Intimately. Her light would flicker, as he felt her anxiety rise.

There had been noticeable improvement, but the dark place memories that interfered with what she needed most to radiate fully still lingered. He smiled gently and brightened his light. She returned the smile, and her radiance solidified again. She tilted her head back and gripped him as she let out her sigh of ecstasy, light brightening intensely. He followed her.

They cuddled as their lights faded, and her skin responded as he kissed her forehead and caressed her. This moment was bittersweet. He sat up, turned toward her, reached out his hands, and gently pulled her close to him. She had come far but was not ready for more. There was a journey she must make.

"It's time," he said, looking at her with kindness in his eyes, and smiled.

"Time for what?" she asked curiously.

"It is time for your healing to continue, without my interference," he answered. "I've heard you when you said you are not ready, and I must be strong enough to do what is right."

He raised his hands, outstretched, to each side. His bluish-white light radiated from his cracks and scars, pain apparent on his face. This time, something she'd not witnessed before began to shine.

From the center of his forehead, she noticed another light faintly glowing. Brighter. Brighter. It was a deep amethyst color, radiating from his mind. At the same time, she noted an ever-brightening ruby red glow pulsing in the middle of his chest. Thump. Thump. Thump. From each palm arose balls of opalescent light. They began to spin, and a play of light danced on the walls of the room, as his natural radiance interacted with the opalescence. He stared at her, tears streaming from his eyes, pain and joy fighting for dominance in his eyes. The amethyst, ruby, and opalescent balls of light slowly left him and joined one another in a spinning ball of magnificence. Amethyst, ruby, and pearly luster fought for dominance, as the dancing colors on the wall displayed the entire spectrum of color.

He brought his hands up to encompass the spinning ball of light. She gazed at him in amazement. Tears were welling up in her eyes. The ball of light slowly made its way toward her chest. As it entered her being, she could feel a tingling sensation. He smiled, as the colors of the ball transformed to an emerald light, bright within her, and then slowly shrank deep inside her. The remaining radiance faded, and the room returned to normal.

"That is for you," he said calmly.

"What is it?" she asked.

"It is the purest gift I can give you. It is the combined essence of my thoughts, feelings, hopes, wants, and desires for you and your life. One might say it is love."

She seemed nervous upon hearing the word.

He continued, "Do not let that word scare you. That is what most might call it, but it is a love of you as a unique, radiant being. It is a pure gift because I give it freely to you without expecting it to be returned. You cannot use it now, because it must grow inside of you. It must well up, and in time, radiate so deeply and strongly that you cannot contain it. That will not occur today, and may never be with me. I have no expectation other than that when you do give it away, make sure it is to someone most deserving of it from you. That may take a great deal of time."

She smiled as tears fell from her eyes.

He raised his right hand to wipe away the tears from her cheeks and kissed her forehead.

"It is now time for me to go, but whenever and wherever you need me, I will be there. That will never change. What is between us may or may not ever be, but that will not change how I feel. When the time comes, give that gift to whomever you choose, as long as that person is deserving of it. Now, I must go."

A faint light appeared in him as he slowly faded from her sight.

"Never forget that your name means Victorious," he whispered.

Then, silence.

FEAR

Labor had lasted for twelve hours. He had raced around, providing ice chips, towels, kisses, interacting with the nurses. They had all commented that he was the most attentive soon-to-be father they had ever seen. The excitement of meeting his daughter fueled him. She was almost here. As the doctor kept having the mother push, he awaited the birth. Their families waited in the hall; the anticipation was eating at him. He was excited. The birthing staff continued bringing the new infant into the world. The mother cursed, as was considered normal.

Finally, with a new bawling sound, a new baby. The nurses weighed and measured her, then had the mother hold her. They swaddled her and then asked him if he wished to hold his new daughter. He did.

The nurse placed her in his arms, overcoming him with emotion. Was he going to drop her? A flood overtook him; a lifetime of feelings and emotions were installing, like software on a computer. He imagined sleepless nights, crying, diapers, sickness, items too easy to swallow. He worried about SIDS, abductions, skinned knees, broken bones, and painful screams. Within the swirls of memories that had yet to come, he heard laughter and saw smiles. More images flew at him, jamming themselves into his brain, burning their impressions into his psyche. The images continued, opening his eyes, heart, mind, and soul, occasionally causing him to wince. He was uncomfortable. The images continued into her teens and adulthood. Pain, love, loss—would a man hurt or abuse her? Could her father help? Could her father prepare her? All of this over the first few moments of holding her the first time.

This man. A former Marine, who pursued anything and everything, suddenly realized what had happened. The universe was transforming this father into a dad. It had instilled in him something he had not known for the twenty-seven years before. He now knew fear.

HEAD VERSUS HEART

All was quiet in the command center, the brain of the entire system. A version of himself sat at a console. Respiration, circulation, motor function, everything within the system observed from this place. The man glanced, briefly, over his shoulder at a vast apparatus with arcing electricity, and a multi-axis chair. With each current arc, the chair turned slowly. In the center of the chair appeared holograms of images and memories: the past and the present.

An observation screen dropped from the ceiling with the press of a button. Audio piped through the room, and video of a chamber appeared. Thump, Thump, Thump. He could view every angle of the chamber. It was the heart of the entire system. All looked well as he left the main room to fetch more coffee.

Inside the chamber, seated in front of large steel doors, was another version of the man. He had light flames coursing over his scarred body, a joyless look decorating his face. Behind him, the heart of the operation continued to beat. Thump, Thump, Thump. Above the thumping was a focal point designed to send and receive, but the closed steel doors blocked it. He sighed. He did not know how long it had been.

At the center of the spinning multi-axis chair, new images began to appear—a radiant beauty. Laughing, smiling, talking, and more. Thump. Thump. Thump. Thump. Thump. Thump. Thump. Thump. Thump. The audio in the chamber, from the heart of the system, was picking up its pace. The arcing electricity around the chair began to arc more violently, crackling.

In the chamber, the scarred, fiery man turned to see the beating heart of the system. It pounded fervently. A loud clanking sound was heard, echoing throughout the chamber. He turned toward the large steel doors in awe, as he witnessed the doors opening. He stood facing the entryway, clenching his jaw and fists, as he peered through the ever-growing crack between the doors swinging outward. He wondered how long it had been since he'd last made a connection with the mechanism behind him. Flames coursed over him, burning hotter as the doors opened wider.

A beam of blue-white light entered the chamber and struck the focal point. The thumping was deafening. The steel doors ended their opening sequence with a thud, light streaming into the room. The man ignited, and the chamber filled with fire, light, heat, passion, excitement, joy, and love. The flames rolled over him, circled the inside of the chamber, and made their way to the focal point. It received the light from the outside and sent the amalgamation of light, heat, fire, and emotion outward. The thumping was the loudest and strongest he'd heard in a while. A smile appeared on his face as tears streamed down. The warmth of the incoming connection caused his chest to glow as he generated a burning desire.

In the command center, the man returned to the control room and noticed the loud, rapid thumping. He looked over at the chair and saw the images, and now memories were joining in with them. A look of distress painted itself on his face, as the mug came crashing to the ground. He could see the images and memories of the radiant beauty.

"No, no, no. Not again," the command center attendant said as he raced toward the multi-axis chair.

He pressed a button on the harness holding the chair, causing it to stop spinning long enough for him to climb into it. He strapped himself into the chair and grasped at the handles, each with buttons near his thumbs. The chair started to spin again. He pressed the button at his left thumb, and past images entered into the center of the chair. A different face. One from the past. A memory of pain entered the fray of pictures, as the chair spun faster.

The man in the chamber burned as bright as the sun. He laughed, smiled, cried tears of joy at the warmth of the connection from the other side of the open portal. He reciprocated, sending the same pleasant feelings outward. The chamber rumbled with the different sounds of the thumping and rumbling flames.

"I forgot what this felt like," he whispered as he burned.

"No, no, no. Not again," came over the loudspeaker in the chamber. "If something happens to you, we'll all perish."

"No. Don't. I can handle it; I always manage to survive it. We cannot live without this. Please!" he pleaded as his fire burned.

The man in the command center worked the controls of the multi-axis chair, spinning faster and faster. More and more past images and pain entered to blend with the current, pleasant images and memories.

"I must regain control of the doors," he said as the dizzying effects of the chair took its toll on him.

The chair spun, faster and faster, as more and more memories and thoughts entered the image soup, into which he peered. He was determined to regain control of the doors. The chair was the only known way.

"Don't do it. Please!" the imprisoned man heard from the speakers. "We all need this. Trust me."

"We cannot risk it. We do not want the pain."

"Remember all of the good memories. There are so many. It's not just pain. There is so much more."

The chair spun faster. More thoughts, images, memories, pain entered into the equation.

In the chamber, a grating sound echoed, and the doors started to move, slowly, inward. A look of despair crept onto the burning man's face.

"No, don't. This one is different. You are using memories from the past that did not involve a connection. Let the doors stay open," the man shouted.

"We cannot risk it. The steel protects you. You are too important to risk," the voice from above boomed.

The burning man ran towards the doors, pressing at each in a feeble attempt to keep them open. Slowly, they got closer and closer; he had a hand on each door.

"STOP!!!" he cried as he fell to his knees.

The narrowing doors caused the incoming connection to grow thin. The burning man's flames flickered as he knelt there, crying. The chamber's temperature cooled, and the light stream stopped with the slamming of the doors. The flames snuffed out, as the focal point stopped sending the emotions and heat. He pounded at the gates; echoes rattled through the chamber.

"Why did you have to overthink it? We would have been fine," he said, between tears.

"It was for the best. It could have killed you," the voice responded.

"I've survived them all. These scars are reminders of both joy and pain," he responded as he looked over every single scar.

"We couldn't risk it."

"But it is so much worse when the doors are closed," he whispered as he collapsed into tears.

TIRED

He sat in his wooden rocker; the creaking of the chair pronounced. Andie, his beautiful mutt, lay on the porch next to him. It was near sundown, and the canvas of the sky did not disappoint today. He looked over at the empty rocker on the other side of the little wooden table. A smile crept onto his face, but there was sadness in it. Andie raised her head to look at him. She sensed something deep within him.

The smile grew out of many things. The beauty of the impending sunset, the companionship of the dog, and the memories he played through as he stared at the empty chair. It belonged to no one. It never had. He had crafted it with an image of a kind soul he hoped to have fill it. Andie whimpered as she moved closer to him, draping her snout over his foot.

"I love you too, girl."

He closed his eyes and played through his memories. Joys. Sorrows. Pain. Regret. Accomplishments. Failures. Strength. A smile—the sum of it all. He thought of his daughters and their children, looking forward to their next visit. The little joys that reminded him that although there was an empty chair, he had still known love.

Every crush he'd had, every love he shared, every kiss—he remembered. Memories of laughter, emotional abuse so many years ago, and his recovery; he smiled. Long kisses with past love now lost. A smile. Memories of intimacy with those whom he'd never get to share more than a few moments. He smiled.

He'd succeeded at so many things, except the thing he wanted most. But he had loved. There was no question he had loved. He let his kind blue eyes and friendly smile do most of the talking in life. The wrinkles in the corner of his eyes communicated a life of authenticity.

Andie lifted her head from his foot and slowly stood next to him, placing her head on his knee, expressing concern with a whimper. He put his hand on her head and smiled at her.

The chair was a dichotomy of sorts. A symbol of one who never was, and of so many who were forever a part of his soul's tapestry. Each a thread woven into him with mastery, leaving an indelible impression. Especially the one who caused his soul to yearn for more. He was always painfully aware of time, and timing would be his curse. He found joy and gratitude in those memories, too.

He stood, and Andie looked at him. Her head slightly tilted as she whimpered again. They took their time as they walked into the house and into his room. He changed into his sleepwear and Andie climbed onto the bed, ready to cuddle him.

He lay down, exhausted. His eyes closed, and he remembered angelic laughs, fantastic voices, beautiful smiles, soft kisses… everything. A smile. The smile slowly faded. His breath slowed.

Andie looked at him, sensing his world-weariness and thought, *You've been tired a long time. Rest now.*

With that, he let out a long, last breath, followed by silence. Andie cuddled his chest and cried.

VAST

She was a vast ocean.

The depths of her love unending and directionless; powerful feelings and emotions felt with each wave.

It was her way.

He was a battleship.

Cutting through the surface of the tumult with his gentle power and presence was his way.

He penetrated the surface, his protection always evident, and his guidance felt with his purpose.

Whether calm or a raging storm, he was to maintain course, to guide and protect her.

Her nature to give her love, its depths uncharted, and occasionally challenge him with her storms of passion and unbridled love.

His reason was the rudder that guided them through those moments when the tempest seemed so intense that the ship might sink.

With her intensity, he would penetrate more deeply with his bow to again remind her of his strong presence and his sheer will to remain on course, at all costs.

When serenity was to return, she could feel him there, unwavering in his purpose.

He would continue exploring her love, steady in his course until time ceased.

She would know his love and he hers.

VI

PART SIX

Preparation

FIRST OF YOUR LAST

What would you do if today was your last?
Stop. Think. Dwell.
Never to wake again.
Never to see the stars above.
Never to hear a laugh, see a smile, feel a breeze, or hear a thunderstorm while cuddled up next to someone special.
Never to whisper sweet nothings to a significant other.
Stop. Think. Dwell.
What would you do if today's sunrise and sunset were your last?
Have you seen mountains that touch the clouds?
Have you seen the sunrise over one ocean and set over another on the same day?
Does it make you think about where your time and attention go?
Do you even know where they go?
Today is new, and it is your last.
Would you smile more?
Would you see all the wonder around you?

Would you kiss until you could not breathe?

Would you hug until you could not hold?

Would you love unconditionally, uncontrollably?

Would your words matter?

Would people know how much they meant to you when you are gone?

Would you matter to them?

Stop. Think. Dwell.

Every day is a new day. A new start. A new chance to try, to do, to be.

What would you do today?

Are you awake?

Today is your only day.

Everything that you say or do has an impact on those around you. Make sure it is a positive one.

It is your first.

It is your last.

It is the first of your last.

PROFUNDITY OF LOVE

Love, affection, caring; I've long believed whatever word used to describe something between people was a choice. After the chemicals calmed down, there was a bond. However, there are times where there is something profound in the soul. A yearning. Therein lies the profundity of love. Something so rare and so deep it hurts. To those who have never experienced it, it is a blessing and a curse; those who have know it is earth-shattering. It changes one at the core of their being. To have experienced it only once, in passing, is enough to ruin the soul for anything less. Waiting for the awakening that may never come is a fate worse than death.

BE SEEN

To look with more than the eyes.

To listen with more than the ears.

To touch with more than our hands.

These are the things that make us seen, heard, and
touched at the core of our being.

HEROICALLY HONEST

Excellent communication—whether writing, speech, or touch—is honest. Honesty first must occur within oneself, then with everyone else. Honesty is scary. It is vulnerable. Open. It exposes the jugular. The underbelly. The soul. It is stripping away armor, pretension, false truths, false lies, and exposing ourselves, often to others. That is scary. Honesty brings with it authenticity, however, and authenticity brings peace. When we allow ourselves to be seen, genuinely, it is frightening, because we could feel pain. However, the only way to truly experience the wonders of interacting with others is through honesty, and thus vulnerability. When we close ourselves off out of fear, we also close ourselves off to the very things that make this life wondrous and invigorating. We deny ourselves connecting with other human beings, and it is in those connections we thrive, grow, and love. To face fear takes courage. Be honest. Be heroically honest.

LOVE IS A GIFT

Love. It is a feeling that inspires songs, poems, movies, acts of kindness, romance, and so much more. It is something that we all want to feel and receive. It is a dichotomy in that it is at once the most beautiful and most excruciating feeling one can have. To feel butterflies and aches. To have hopes and fears. To experience joys and losses. It can cause the best of us to feel anxiety and feel like we are going crazy.

With this amazing, overpowering, and somewhat sickening feeling come expectations, often unspoken, that lead to loss, pain, and heartache. How could this be, for love is wonderful? It is because we are not responsible custodians of what love is, truly. It is more than a feeling; it is also a choice. When held in both the heart and mind with conscious, intentional effort, it becomes even more powerful and amazing. We take the time to think lovingly and kindly of those who are special to us, making sure that we listen from the perspective of what someone else might want or need. Doing so may create a conflict in our innermost desires, but we must be honest.

Love must be noble. It must be pure. It must be selfless. It must be a gift. It must be treasured. When we love someone, it must be our gift to them for who they are, without condition or expectation. That is scary. Imagine, though, loving someone so unconditionally that you want for them the very best. Do it without expectation. Think about loving, because you can, not because you want something. Loving for the sake of love is freeing. It allows you to smile at that person in good times and bad, and always love them. It enables you to give, freely, of yourself. When focusing on giving, a funny thing starts to happen. You feel more at peace. You feel happier because you love for the sake of loving.

This is an important thing to understand, because love must remain selfless. Letting go is also a noble act of love. We may feel sorrow and loss, but to indeed have a love for another is to accept what that person may need and love so much that you let them go. Do so with the hope they get everything they wish for themselves, that they experience joy and happiness. Smile and thank them for your time with them. It won't be easy, but when the tears subside, you will have that pure love and the comfort it carries with it.

Love is not about ownership or expectation. It is a gift. Give it. Then, let them go as any other person could freely do with their gifts from you.

WHISPER

Shhh. Do you hear that?

No, not the sounds around you—but rather what is underneath it all.

Under the distractions of the day-to-day is where the truth lies.

That is if you are attending.

Can you hear it?

Do you want to?

Close your eyes, and quiet the noise around you.

Quiet your brain and bestill your heart.

Listen.

Can you hear it now?

Not with your ears, but with your heart.

Listen.

It is there.

It is faint, but it is there.

It is but a whisper.

The Universe is calling to you, always.

Are you listening?

Do you hear it?

Do you feel it?

Do you want to hear and feel it?

It is there, the faint whisper, calling out to you.

It echoes through the vastness of time and space, knowing no limits that we place on ourselves.

I've heard the whisper, and I feel it.

It has filled me up with what is and what can be.

All other things have melted away.

Do you hear the *thump, thump, thump* echoing there?

A beating. A burning. A yearning.

Those sensations have sounds.

Listen.

Hear it?

It is a whisper.

One that has made me smile.

I am waiting there.

Can you hear the whisper?

Do you want to listen to it?

VII

PART SEVEN

She Who Touched my Heart (My Song)

RIPPLE

Every person you meet is the universe providing an opportunity.
Take time to smile, talk, laugh, and enjoy.
You never know if they will be the ripple in the pond that changes your life.

BATHE IN BEAUTY

Your smile is like the sun, radiant and warm.
It lights up the room and scares away storms.
Add a lip bite to boot, and it is easy to see
What your smile does to others—especially me.
Your eyes are profound, the gate to your soul.
Yes, beautiful, but understand their role.
They communicate your thoughts, your heart, and your needs.
In them, I see your beauty and your vulnerability.
Your laugh is a song—a concert of sorts.
It rises to angelic heights and is sweet with its snorts.
Used in conjunction, they hide who you are.
Someone of beauty, rivaling that of a star.
A beacon of light in a dark, painful world.
A beautiful woman, a fun-loving girl.
When you snuggle in close and let the world disappear,
I hope you know what it is that I see, feel, and hear.
When I steal away a kiss or dance with you in the hall,
I'm trying to freeze time so that I may bathe in it all.

TODAY

I don't know what tomorrow will bring.

So, let us not think about that.

Instead, let us focus on this.

I want today, with you.

I want you today—every day.

SO MUCH

There is so much I want to say to you if you let me. How do I articulate the thoughts in a way that will not cause you to push me away?

When you hear them, will you panic in your head, but secretly be comforted in your heart?

Will it register warmly, but be responded to coldly? Is that inner conflict I see in your eyes, struggling to accept or even cherish what you see before you?

Is the hard exterior just the way you protect against the fear of being abandoned, betrayed, or hurt?

Is the assertion that you are not sentimental contrary to your innermost desire to be safe, embraced, accepted, and loved unconditionally?

If my words are too much to hear, then listen to my eyes. Feel my energy, and the message my touch conveys.

Let my actions, my presence, and my attention speak. Teach me how to communicate in your language, so our wires never cross.

Listen to my smile, my eyes, my touch, and my silence if it will help you feel safe and believe.
There is so much I want to say to you.

CONVERGE

Time—perceived to be linear, but is nonlinear.

The past, present, and future are all available to us.

When I close my eyes, I can see you at three points.

Then. Now. Someday.

I see fear and pain, rest and healing, and joy and happiness.

They are all you.

Different times, different places, but all here.

Right now.

Remove the constraint of time.

Look beyond, and note that you are at all points.

Right now.

Be present in the moment and enjoy it.

Embrace the idea that everything that is happening is happening right now.

Do not think of what should have been, what you should be doing, and what might be later.

Focus on now.

Let time melt away, and let all of you—past, present, and future—converge.

Now, you have fear and pain, rest and healing, and
joy and happiness.
Right now.

BLACK HOLE

The problem with being an optimist and a romantic is believing in grand gestures, and generally thinking everything will work out. The idea of traveling hundreds of miles to catch a smile, steal away a passionate kiss, get warmed by an embrace, or to stare into each other's eyes while making love puts a giddy smile on one's face. It is a tale of two people coming together against all odds—a story to tell grandchildren one sunny spring afternoon when they ask *how did you meet?*

Every phone call, flower delivery, and visit seems to matter more, because it is more than just a visit down the road and around the corner. It cannot be taken for granted in the usual ways. While there are challenges technology can help bridge, seeing each other is better when our eyes meet, finally knowing what the stomach feels. Hunger. Hunger for the one we wish to see with no filters or restrictions. The sight of them approaching, smiles broad, and the desire mutually apparent by the way each person bites their lips makes the stomach tickle with butterflies.

It is also a measure of time and distance, when able to embrace and subsequently kiss to close a space not understood by many.

Time ceases to move forward while two souls come together with a kiss as passionate as their first. The wide, joyous smiles and abundant laughter offset the sigh of relief that follows. All is right in the world again.

The hours of conversation, the playful touching, the bodies coming together as one, followed by the peaceful sleep and subtle sounds of breathing are music that makes one ask *what is the name of this song?*

For the romantic, these moments are meaningful. Powerful. Hopeful. Sexy.

For the optimist, these moments are steps toward a future filled with happiness. Moments. Memories. Imagination.

The problem with being an optimist and a romantic? Never imagining a day without that person. When that day comes, the hole that spans head, life, and heart is like that of a black hole. Something that not even light can escape.

ALL OF YOU

I miss your blue eyes, so wild and free,
And the way that you blush when you stare.
I miss your soft lips, and the passionate kisses,
While running my hands through your hair.
I miss your lip bite when I gaze at you,
And your smile that ensues, how it beams.
I miss the witty banter while talking all night,
And your "ugly laugh," snorting it seems.
I miss pulling you close, grabbing your ass when we kiss,
And letting the world fade away.
These are a few of the things that I miss.
I think of you every day.
The way you respond when my lips touch your skin;
Exploring it from head to toe.
I miss the sounds you make when you take all of me in,
And the radiance of your glow.
I miss how aroused you get with my touch, stroke,
and kiss;
Our bodies and souls so bare.
It's all of these things, all of you, my dear,
That make me wish I were there.

GRIEF

The longing, sadness, and emptiness I feel are profound. Tears fall from my eyes. I'd say for no reason, but there is one. You. Moments with you. I miss flirting, talking, laughing, touching, and fucking you. When I am mindful and spend time with myself to bathe in this feeling, it becomes overwhelming. I can still hear your voice and laugh. I can even see your smile. I can see you looking at me with hunger in your eyes, but I can also see hurt. I can feel your touch and energy. I can hear you snore, and sigh, and moan. I cry. I am grieving you. I am lamenting a divergence in what I can see and have experienced, and where we are. My soul is aching for yours. We are connected. I know I will survive this. I will smile and cry because our moments were joyous, and I am filled with sorrow at the thought that there may be no more. I miss everything about you. So, I grieve.

MISS THAT KISS

I miss that kiss. You know the kind.

Where our heartbeats skip and it blows our minds.

My hand around your waist, pulling you near.

The lip bite, subtle smile, and the sighs that we hear.

Our eyes slowly shut, as the distance does close.

The light touch of lips, and slight brush of the nose.

My other hand cradles your head at the top of your neck.

My thumb caresses your cheek, as we kiss and we peck.

Our tongues do a dance, the rhythm's just right.

Our bellies have butterflies, we could do this all night.

A giggle, a smile, a lip bite or two.

These are what I miss about those kisses with you.

The goosebumps you get on your arms, neck, and spine.

In those moments, I'm yours and you're mine.

We manage to part, our eyes in a gaze.

That beautiful smile, and that dizzying haze.

Your cheeks are flush red, and your skin is on fire.

We kiss yet again, both on fire with desire.

It's soft at first, then deep, but not rushed.

Nothing else matters, this kiss is a must.

I close my eyes while I'm remembering this.
Do you feel the same? Do you miss that kiss?

WHAT I WANT FOR YOU

Do you know what I want for you? Happiness. I want laughter and smiles for you. A deep sense of belonging and acceptance of who you are today and who you'll be in the future. I understand that over time people change, but what I want is for you to know what unconditional love is. I want you to know that you do not have to be perfect. You will never have to be better than your best and that if your best is curled up in a ball, so be it. I want comfort for you. Solace in times of need. A strong belief you have love and support.

I also want independence and interdependence for you. Combined, they bring peace. Depend on yourself and another. Be comfortable on your own or with another, without relying on them. There is a difference.

I want you to experience goosebumps and butterflies. I want you to experience the tingling sensation you get when someone truly sees you and works hard to connect with you: mind, body, and soul. I want you to feel desired. Desired for your thoughts, your actions, your beauty, for being you.

When you are sad or overwhelmed, I want you to feel as if everything will be okay. It would help if you didn't feel the need to be rescued because you are strong and will overcome. However, I want you to know that watching you persevere and conquer things is one of the fuels that light my fire. I wish for you to know that *you got this* and that *I got you*.

I want you to know that you are enough. Not in a way that discourages self-improvement, but rather in the way that focuses on those inner fears. Even when you think you are not enough, you are. Know it.

I want there to be affection, kisses, cuddles, and a meaningful life of feeling appreciated. Those things may mean something different to you than to others, but having someone willing to learn you and love you for everything you are now and in the future—this is what I want for you.

I want serenity for you. There is work to be done that only you can do. I want you to feel the success of that and to be cheered along on your journey by someone who will not do it for you. You are on a journey of healing and patience and will not be perfect or ever complete. I want for you to stare into the eyes of kindness and have those eyes reflect you everything you should see of yourself.

What I want for you is all of that, and I want you to know I want it so much for you that it does not matter if it's with me. Happiness is what I want for you.

VIII

PART EIGHT

Me

RAGING STORM

There is a raging storm, deep inside,
Something I often try to hide
To protect those who travel near.
It will scare them, is what I fear.
To feel so deeply with all of me.
To think so deeply, about all I see.
Love and pain intertwined.
They are the same, unconfined.
They bleed over into my soul.
Would someone run, if they were to know?
I am protecting them, I tell myself.
Or protecting me? I ask myself.
The pain runs deep. It is anguish, you see.
To have died in my soul with a beckoning plea.
Now, the head has a say as to who sees what.
Can anyone handle an emotional glut?
Will I crush someone with all of the feels?
These thoughts are what powers the head's engine,
spinning its wheels.
Will they hurt if I show nothing at all?

Likely the case, so decide to go small.

Smile, be kind, keep a calm face,

And hide the raging storm in my soul's deepest place.

BARE

Have you ever met someone who so wholly set you aflame in the depths of your being that it consumed you and burned away all the facades and beliefs you had of yourself? I have. When I met her, there was an instant and deep connection. We spent hours talking, laughing, joking, and feeling as if we had known each other since childhood. Over the several weeks that followed that fantastic day, we got to know each other, despite physical distance being a tremendous hurdle. When we saw each other again, the conversation and laughter flowed. The banter, sarcasm, energy, sexual tension, and mood were all there. When we consummated the budding relationship that weekend, it was exquisite.

What followed was more of the same. A flow. A connection. However, there was turbulence. We both had traumas in our past. Hers more recent than mine. As my deep, profound, and complete love for her grew, her fear of intimacy led to panic. Push. Pull. Push. Pull. Push.

Heartbreak is where I landed. A sadness of immeasurable depth set in with the loss of a connection I could feel across hundreds of miles. The fire that consumed my mind, body, and soul so completely left me bare to myself. Exposed were pieces of me I had long forgotten, never knew existed, or covered out of fear. In a short time, she reminded me of the things about being a man I had forgotten. She shared fears of hers and I reassured her, but subconsciously I think our energies were communicating.

I had hoped the universe had placed us in each other's path for the remainder of the journey we call life. However, I am coming to slowly understand she may have been the catalyst for growth and healing I needed. Having burned away mechanisms in place since childhood, this wise man stood facing a cowering boy version of himself in the darkest corners of his psyche. Only rough edges remained, and those are what make intimacy genuinely magical. That scared little boy only wants to be loved and accepted as he is. No fear. No shame.

I believe I was only about 80% of the man I needed to be. There are still areas of my life I approach with an "If I do this, then that will happen" mentality. Instead, my focus is turning to the position of "I do this because it is what I want."

I can now say to my young self: Take my hand, young man. I can teach you to be the man you intended to be.

I am thankful to have met her. She taught me about being the man she needed me to be without using words. While I wanted nothing more than for her to feel safe and love with me, she was the savior. She saved me from myself. I continue to send her positive thoughts and energy daily, as well as thoughtful prayers at night. Thank you, my "princess of precious stones," for igniting me so wholly that I lay bare.

I LOVE

Love.

So many things come to mind when we think of this word.

By definition, it is a feeling of strong or constant affection for something.

It elicits other thoughts, ideas, and words like affection, attachment, devotion, passion, desire, longing, and yearning.

Each paints their picture and makes one feel their meaning.

Love.

It is powerful and frightening.

Often, there are limits or bounds to which many adhere.

Conditions for love.

Why?

We often say *I love you because*, and proceed to provide one or numerous reasons as to why we love that person.

Although it is nice to hear, consider the limits we are placing on love.

I love you because.

Is that the only reason?

What if that changes or goes away?

Will love remain?

Let's roll it back, just a bit.

I love you.

Better.

It conveys wholeness, completeness, a belief that the one—in this case, you—are loved.

The implication that it is for being who you are.

However, it is still limiting and conditional.

How?

It is directional and therefore implies there are reasons to love you.

Consider loving, because you can.

Love bravely, completely, and without condition.

Unconditional love.

Let it well up within you, like a volcano ready to explode. There are no bounds or limits.

When I give it to you, it is without condition, parameters, or expectations.

Love in such a way the other person feels free.

I can.

I love.

LABELS

I am a lover, fighter, scientist, CrossFitter, writer,
programmer.

I am logical and emotional.

I am a son, father, man.

I am straight. I love everyone for the unique person
they are.

I am a Christian. A Buddhist. A philosopher.

I am a song.

I feel the energy around me. I see the beauty.

Labels are divisive. Too simple. I am complex.

I reject labels.

The only label I will accept? Me.

CUSP OF SENSITIVITY

I am of two forms. I am complicated.

I will swirl around you, blowing your hair away from your neck.

I am the whisper in your ear.

Take me deep inside you. Breathe me in, and know you are alive.

I am the ideas, lofty in heights.

I am shapeless. You cannot grab me, but you feel me.

I will circle high above, watching and protecting, directing your path.

I am that heady, airy sensation you feel. It is my gift to you.

If you are fire, I will feed you. You burn hot and bright. Our passion is explosive.

I am complicated.

I am the patter you hear outside; smell me just before I arrive.

I will quench thirst and give life.

If you are hard and immovable, I will soften you over time. It is my way.

My surface may seem choppy, but there is more than what you see.

Treat me coldly, and I will freeze you out.

Swim in my love and be swept away.

Be sure you are ready because my depths know no bounds.

Go too deep, and my love just may crush you.

Breathe me or drink me in. I will sustain you.

I am logic.

I am emotion.

I am the cusp of sensitivity.

RECOVERY

Relationships are like working out at the gym. There is a lot that goes into both. There's work, preparation, and the little things that make it all come together. When there is pain, there is a phase of recovery. It hurts. It is important to remember, however, that adequately fueling the mind, body, and soul is imperative. It is fine to wait a bit, to recover, but like working out, that period could be too long. Building occurs while we are recovering, but still feeling a little pain. Do the work. Do it lightly if you have to, but do the work. That is how we build real strength—dedication, repetition, and effort.

In the case where an injury has sidelined you, there is not just the physical aspect, but also the mental roadblocks. Again, do the work. Find your champions and cheerleaders, the people who will push you and hold you accountable. Heal the injury, and slowly begin again. Dedicate yourself to constant improvement. Never get complacent, and remember that resting is not lazy; it is recovery.

LOVE AND LOSS

It is better to have loved and lost than never to have loved at all.

I agree.

It is both the most exciting and excruciating thing one can feel. The trick is to focus on love, most unconditionally. We tend to focus on outcomes and getting attached. Instead, focus on loving someone, respecting them, and accepting that at any time, something could happen to end it. A bus crash, cancer, or a choice to move on. Then, experience grief. Grief is the feeling we experience after love and loss. Don't get so caught up in a person that you forget about love. Love comes from within us and is limitless. It is a gift we choose to give. As a gift, give it without strings. We wouldn't give a gift and expect it returned, so why would we do so with the gift of love?

Mourn the loss, but embrace and acknowledge that you have given love. It will come again.

ACKNOWLEDGMENTS

I want to thank:

Jason and Lauren. Your friendship and insights have been blessings in my life. Thank you for the laughter, conversations, and honest feedback about the events depicted in this book and the works themselves.

Anastacia and Tatiana. My daughters and two hearts, your love and patience, and your enthusiastic support of this book and the healing that needed to occur have been more than I could ever expect. You two are my heart and reminded me through my heartache what love is.

Bill. My brother from another mother. You have always been a sarcastic voice of wisdom. Thank you for reminding me that you love my unwillingness to give up.

Dave. My younger brother. Thank you for your reminding me that dwelling on the past is folly.

To the ladies who inspired this book, thank you. Our time together and experiences with one another were blessings. You have left an indelible mark on my soul.

Ruth. Thank you for the incredible work on developmental editing. Your insights on the raw emotion on the page and how to organize it as an emotional journey were terrific. Thank you for your partnership.

Nicole. Thank you for the additional editing services. Your hard work and partnership helped move along this project.

Danna. Thank you for the fantastic work designing the cover and interior. Your partnership and efforts have helped ease the butterflies of releasing this, my first book.